DRAWINGS
OF
BRITISH PLANTS

DRAWINGS
OF
BRITISH PLANTS

BEING ILLUSTRATIONS OF THE SPECIES OF
FLOWERING PLANTS GROWING NATURALLY
IN THE BRITISH ISLES

BY

STELLA ROSS-CRAIG, F.L.S.

The Herbarium, Royal Botanic Gardens, Kew

PART V

CARYOPHYLLACEAE

LONDON
G. BELL AND SONS LTD
1951

Printed in Great Britain by
The Camelot Press Ltd., London and Southampton

PART V

CARYOPHYLLACEAE

Dianthus armeria L.   Deptford Pink

A, flowering plant; B, lower part of flowering stem; C, upper part of flowering stem; D, scale; E, calyx; F, petal; G, two stamens; H, gynoecium; I, capsule, with part of calyx and withered petals; J, seed, and transverse section of same; K, part of surface of seed, much enlarged.
Petals rose-magenta, paler in throat, blade spotted with white.

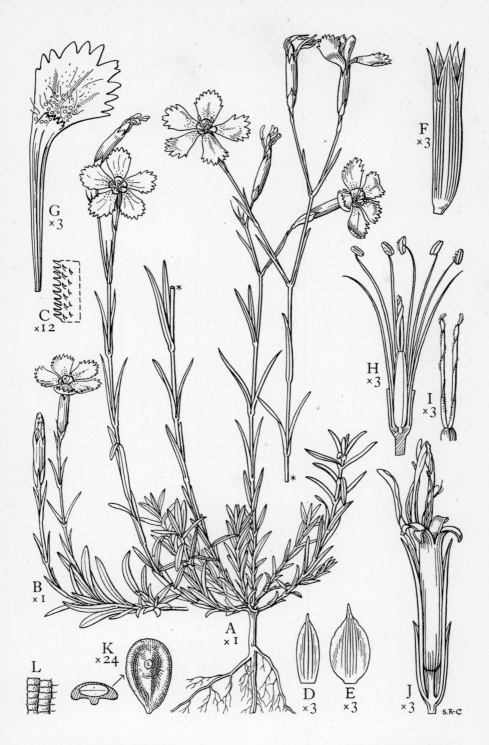

Dianthus deltoides L. Maiden Pink

A, flowering plant; B, part of a smaller plant; C, margin of leaf; D, lower scale; E, upper scale; F, calyx; G, petal; H, androecium, three stamens removed, and gynoecium; I, stigmas after anthesis; J, capsule and withered petals and stamens, the scales and calyx partly cut away; K, seed, and transverse section of same; L, part of surface of seed, much enlarged.

Petals: blade magenta with dark red wavy lines and white spots, claw greenish-white.

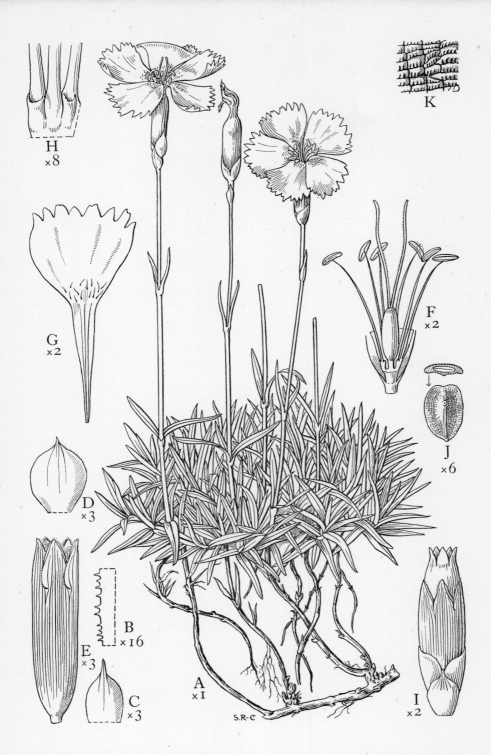

Dianthus gratianopolitanus Vill.   Cheddar Pink
(syn. *D. caesius* Sm.)

A, plant; B, margin of leaf; C, one of the two lower scales; D, one of the two upper scales; E, calyx; F, part of androecium, and the gynoecium; G, petal; H, basal part of three stamens, inner surface; I, scales, calyx, and dehiscing capsule; J, seed, and transverse section of same; K, part of surface of seed, much enlarged.
Petals cerise or pale cerise, with purple hairs at the throat, the claw cream.

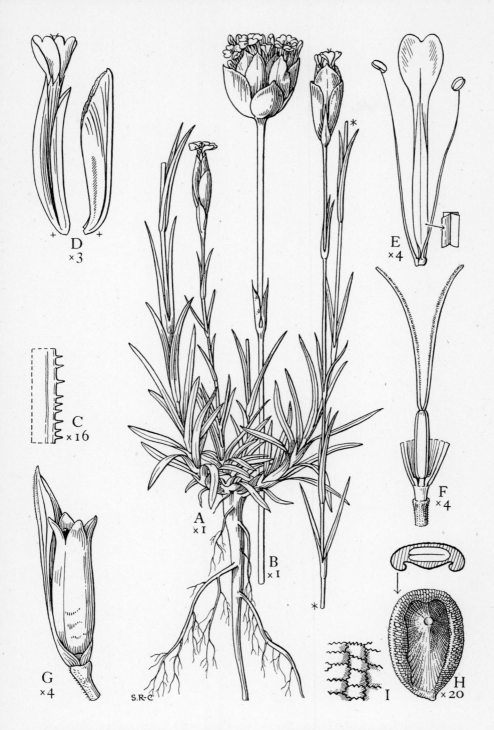

Kohlrauschia prolifera (L.) Kunth   Proliferous Pink, Childing Pink
(syn. *Dianthus prolifer* L., *Tunica prolifera* [L.] Scop.)

A, plant; B, inflorescence from a robust plant; C, margin of leaf; D, one of the inner bracts, and a flower enclosed in two scales; E, petal, and two stamens, and section of the petal-claw; F, apex of pedicel, base of petals and stamens (partly cut away) and gynoecium; G, dehiscing capsule and persistent calyx; H, seed, and transverse section of same; I, part of surface of seed, much enlarged.
Petals cobalt-violet.

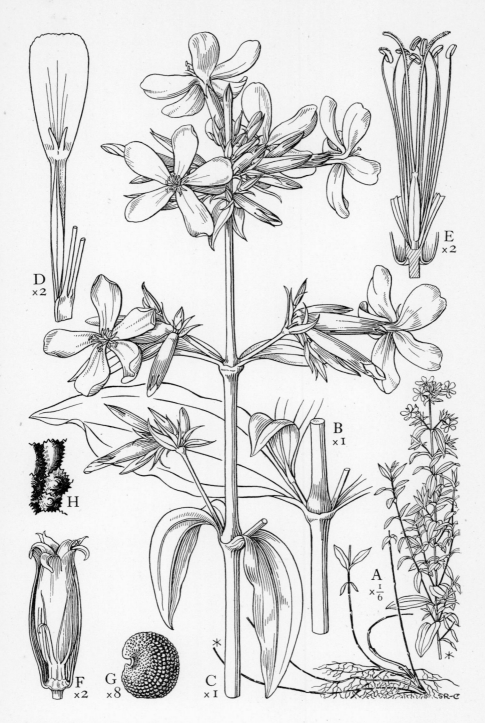

Saponaria officinalis L.   Soapwort

A, plant; B, part of stem two internodes below the flowers; C, inflorescence; D, petal
and base of two stamens; E, flower, three stamens and one petal removed, calyx and
remaining petals cut off near the base; F, dehiscing capsule with remains of petals
and stamens, half of calyx cut away; G, seed; H, part of surface of seed, much enlarged.
Petals cream before unrolling, then white flushed with pink, finally deepening to pale
rose-pink.

Silene cucubalus Wibel   Bladder Campion
(syn. *S. inflata* Sm., *S. vulgaris* Moench)

A and B, upper part of hermaphrodite and female flowering stems; C, leaves from a robust hermaphrodite plant; D, apex of pedicel, basal part of petals and stamens, and ovary; E, petal and two stamens; F, apex of pedicel, stipe, and gynoecium; G, apex of pedicel, base of petals, reduced stamens, and ovary; H, petal and two stamens; I, apex of pedicel, stipe, and gynoecium; J, part of fruiting stem; K, dehiscing capsule, remains of petals and stamens, and half the calyx; L, seed; M, part of surface of seed, much enlarged.
Petals white.

Silene maritima With. Sea Campion

A, base of plant; B, two flowering stems; C, flower, part of calyx cut away, three petals removed, and most of the stamens cut off; D, fruiting stem; E, apex of pedicel, stipe, remains of the petals and stamens, and capsule before dehiscence; F, dehiscing capsule, remains of the petals and stamens, and half the calyx; G, seed; H, part of surface of seed, much enlarged.
Petals white.

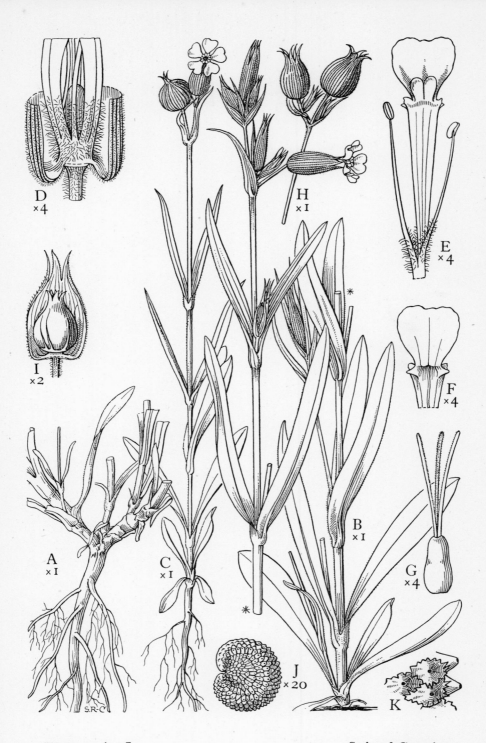

Silene conica L.
Striated Campion

A, base of plant; B and C, two plants; D, basal part of a flower, part of the calyx cut away to show the hairy base of the petals and stamens; E, petal and stamens; F, upper part of petal, outer surface; G, gynoecium; H, part of fruiting stem; I, dehiscing capsule, remains of the petals and stamens, and half the calyx; J, seed; K, part of surface of seed, much enlarged.

Petals rose to pale pink, rarely white. The whole plant puberulous.

v   plate 8

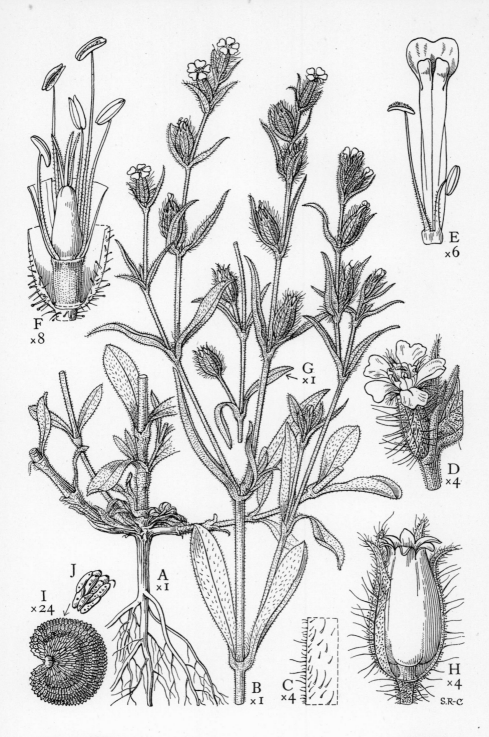

Silene anglica L.   Catchfly

A, base of plant; B, upper part of flowering stem; C, part of margin and upper surface of leaf, the young leaves are glandular; D, apex of a flowering stem; E, petal
and stamens; F, flower, two petals and five stamens removed and part of the other
petals and calyx cut away; G, part of fruiting stem; H, dehiscing capsule and part
of the calyx; I, seed; J, part of surface of seed, much enlarged.
Petals white, or delicately flushed with pink.

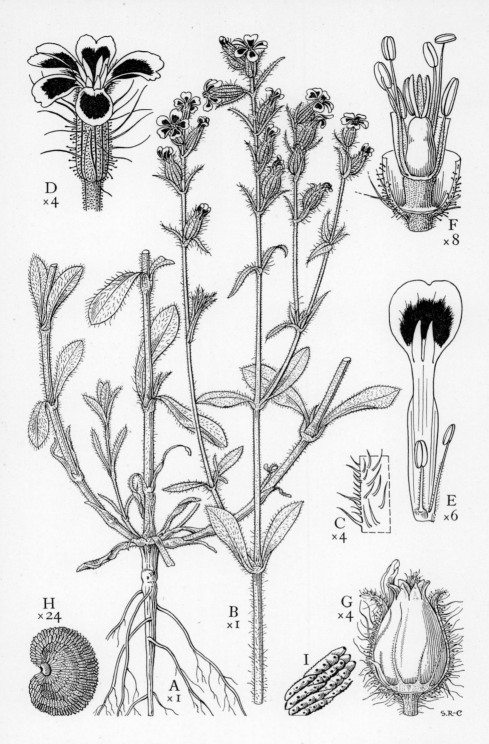

Silene quinquevulnera L.　　　　　　　　　　Spotted Catchfly

A, lower part of plant; B, upper part of flowering stem; C, part of margin and upper surface of leaf; D, flower; E, petal and stamens; F, flower, two petals and four stamens removed, most of calyx and remaining petals cut away; G, dehiscing capsule, remains of the petals and stamens, and half the calyx; H, seed; I, part of surface of seed, much enlarged.

Petals pinkish-white with a large crimson blotch on the blade, corona white.

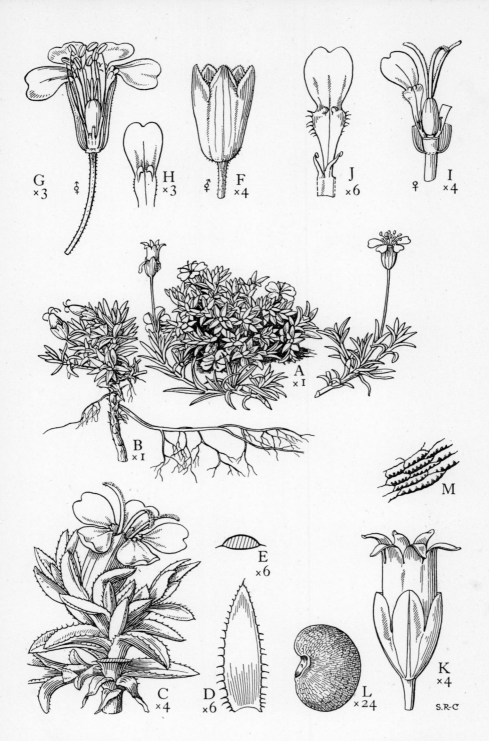

Silene acaulis (L.) Jacq.   Moss Campion

A, part of female plant, and branches from long-pedicelled plants; B, part of short-pedicelled fruiting plant; C, part of flowering stem (female); D, leaf; E, transverse section of leaf; F, calyx; G, flower, part of calyx, one petal and two stamens removed; H, upper part of petal from hermaphrodite flower, inner surface; I, flower, most of the calyx, four petals and two of the vestigial stamens removed; J, petal and two stamens from a female flower; K, dehiscing capsule and persistent calyx; L, seed; M, part of surface of seed, much enlarged.
Petals deep rose, pink, or nearly white.

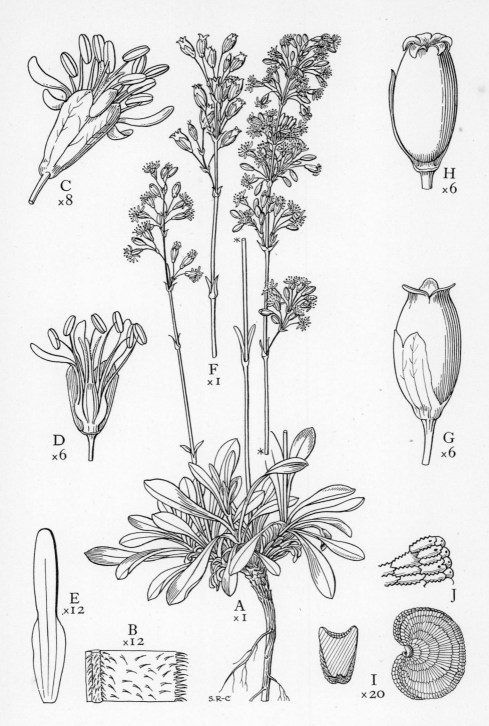

Silene otites (L.) Wibel   Spanish Catchfly

A, flowering plant; B, part of margin and lower surface of leaf, upper surface glabrous;
C, flower; D, flower, part of the calyx, two petals and four stamens removed; E, petal;
F, upper part of fruiting stem; G, dehiscing capsule with the split calyx; H, capsule
and part of calyx; I, seed, and transverse section of same; J, part of surface of seed,
much enlarged.
Petals pale cream, anthers yellow.

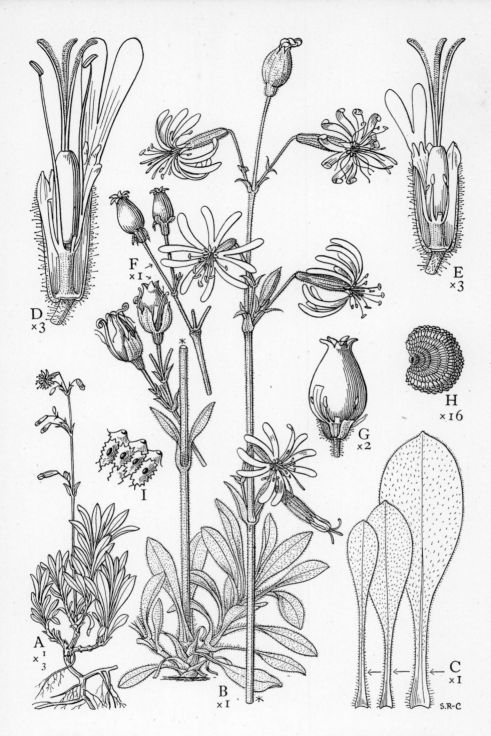

Silene nutans L.   Nottingham Catchfly

A, plant; B, plant with hermaphrodite flowers; C, basal leaves from different plants
to show variation in size and shape; D, hermaphrodite flower, half the calyx, four
petals and eight stamens removed; E, female flower, half the calyx, four petals and
four stamens removed; F, part of fruiting branches from different plants; G, capsule
from female flower with remains of the calyx petals and stamens; H, seed; I, part
of surface of seed, much enlarged.

Petals white, pale greenish-cream on the back; stigmas mauve when exserted.

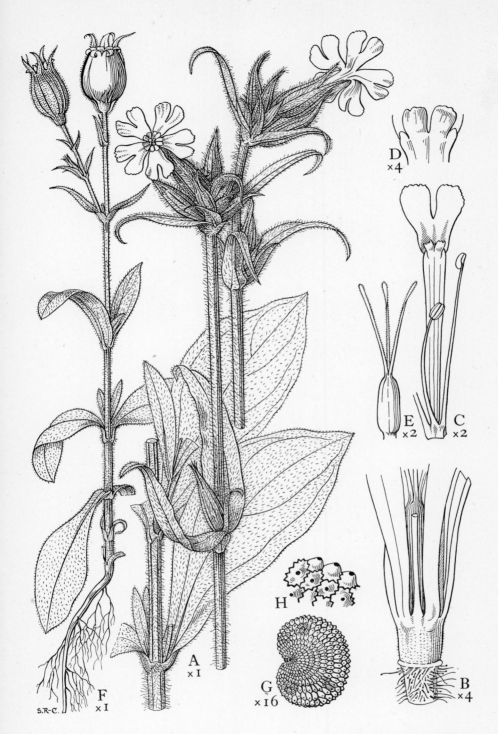

Melandrium noctiflorum (L.) Fr.   Night-flowering Catchfly
(syn. *Silene noctiflora* L.)

A, inflorescences and lower part of main stem from a strong plant; B, lower part of flower, calyx cut off; C, petal and stamens; D, corona at base of blade of petal; E, gynoecium; F, a small plant in fruit; G, seed, the darker areas are sometimes very obscure; H, part of surface of seed, much enlarged.
Petals pale pink, almost white when fully expanded, pale greenish-yellow on the back.

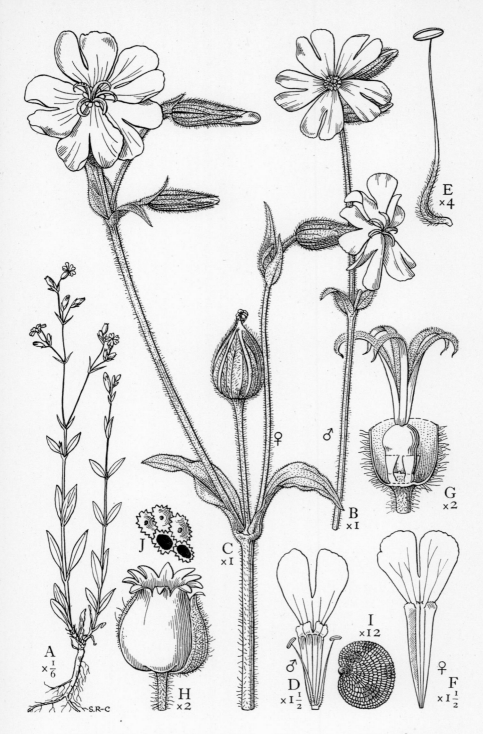

Melandrium album (Mill.) Garcke   White Campion
(syn. *Lychnis alba* Mill.)

A, plant; B, part of inflorescence from male plant; C, upper part of flowering stem
from female plant; D, petal and two stamens from male flower; E, stamen; F, petal
from female flower; G, female flower, most of calyx and petals cut away; H, dehiscing
capsule and part of calyx; I, seed; J, part of surface of seed, showing cells from adja-
cent light and dark areas, much enlarged.
Petals white.

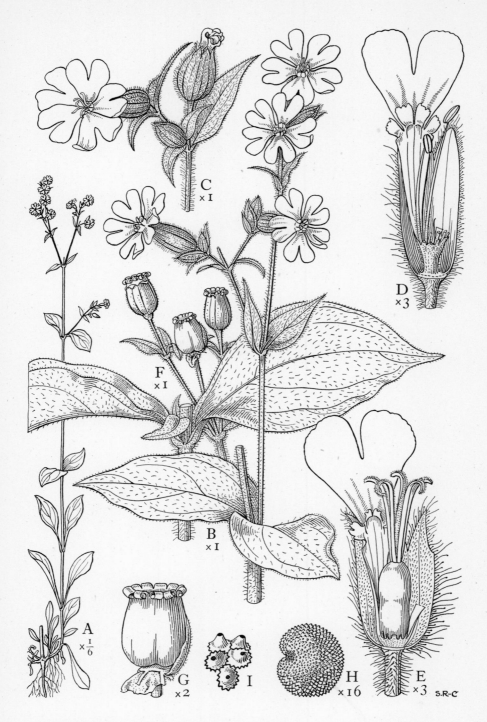

Melandrium dioicum (L.) Coss. & Germ.   Red Campion

(syn. *Melandrium rubrum* [Weig.] Garke; *Lychnis dioica* L.; *L. diurna* Sibth.)

A, part of a plant; B, part of flowering stem from male plant; C, apex of inflorescence from a female plant; D, male flower, half the calyx cut off, four petals and eight stamens removed; E, female flower, half the calyx cut away and four petals removed; F, part of fruiting stem; G, dehiscing capsule; H, seed; I, part of surface of seed, much enlarged.

Calyx green or flushed with red or purple; petals pale to deep rose or rose-cerise.

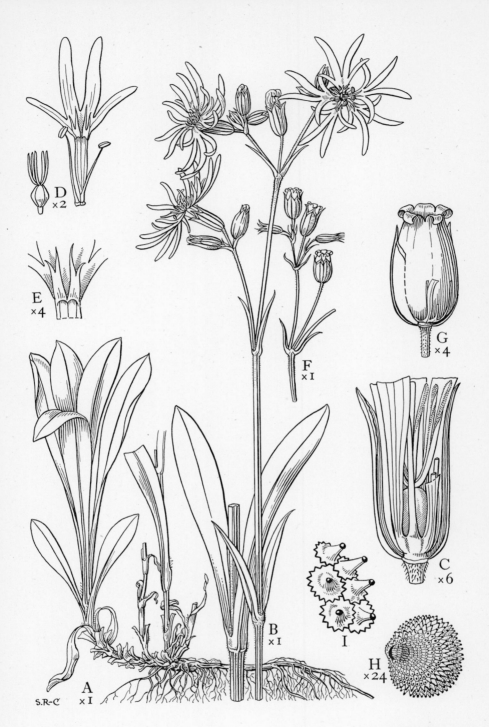

Lychnis flos-cuculi L.　　　　　　　　　　　　　Ragged Robin

A, lower part of plant; B, upper part of flowering stem and a pair of the lower leaves;
C, flower, half the calyx cut away and upper part of petals and stamens cut off; D,
petal, two stamens, and gynoecium; E, part of petal, showing the corona; F, part of
fruiting stem; G, dehiscing capsule, and part of calyx; H, seed; I, part of surface of
seed, much enlarged.
Petals rose-coloured.

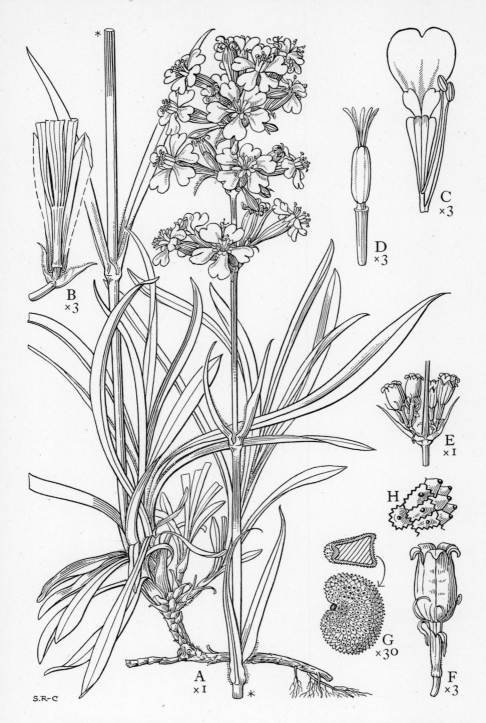

Viscaria vulgaris Bernh.   Red German Catchfly
(syn. *Lychnis viscaria* L.)

A, flowering plant; B, flower, half the calyx cut away and upper part of the petals and
stamens cut off; C, petal and two stamens; D, gynoecium on its long stipe; E, part of
fruiting stem; F, dehiscing capsule and remains of calyx petals and stamens; G, seed,
and transverse section of same; H, part of surface of seed, much enlarged.
Petals cerise, the corona pale mauve.

v plate 18

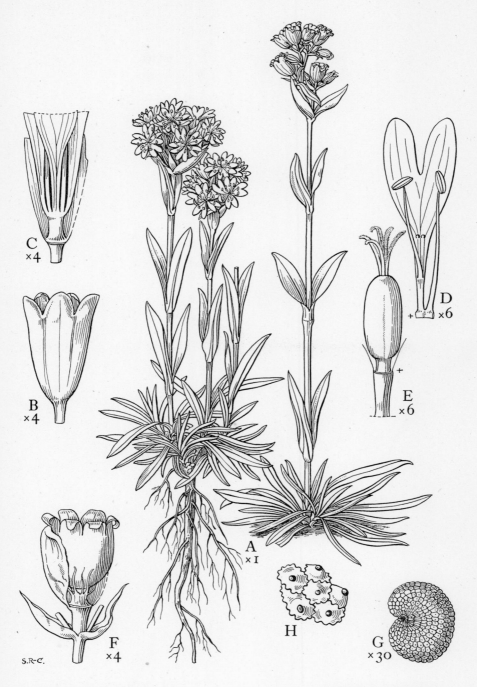

C ×4

B ×4

F ×4

S.R.C.

A ×1

H

G ×30

D ×6

E ×6

Viscaria alpina (L.) Don   Red Alpine Catchfly
(syn. *Lychnis alpina* L.)

A, a flowering plant and a fruiting plant; B, calyx; C, lower part of flower, half the calyx cut away; D, petal and two stamens; E, gynoecium and stipe; F, branch of infructescence, part of calyx cut away to show the dehiscing capsule and remains of petals and stamens; G, seed; H, part of surface of seed much enlarged.
Petals rose.

Agrostemma githago L.
(syn. *Lychnis githago* [L.] Scop.)

Corn Cockle

A, plant; B, upper part of flowering stem, a young flower, pair of leaves from lower part of stem, and a rosette leaf; C, petal and stamens, and base of petal to show flap-like outgrowths; D, gynoecium; E, capsule, and part of calyx; F, seed; G, part of surface of seed much enlarged.

Petals deep to pale magenta-cerise, lighter or whitish in the throat, lines blue-black, shining grey-mauve on the back.

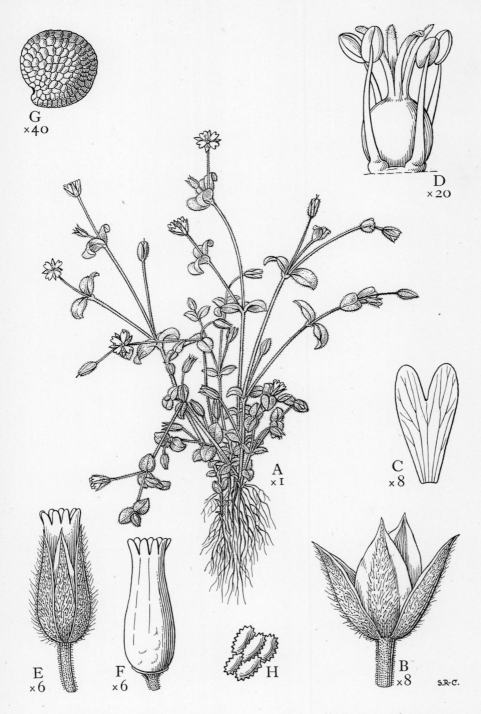

G ×40

D ×20

A ×1

C ×8

E ×6

F ×6

H

B ×8

S.R·C.

Cerastium tetrandrum Curtis   Mouse-ear Chickweed

A, plants; B, calyx and upper part of pedicel; C, petal; D, androecium and gynoecium;
E, dehiscing capsule and calyx; F, capsule; G, seed; H, part of surface of seed much
enlarged.
Petals white.

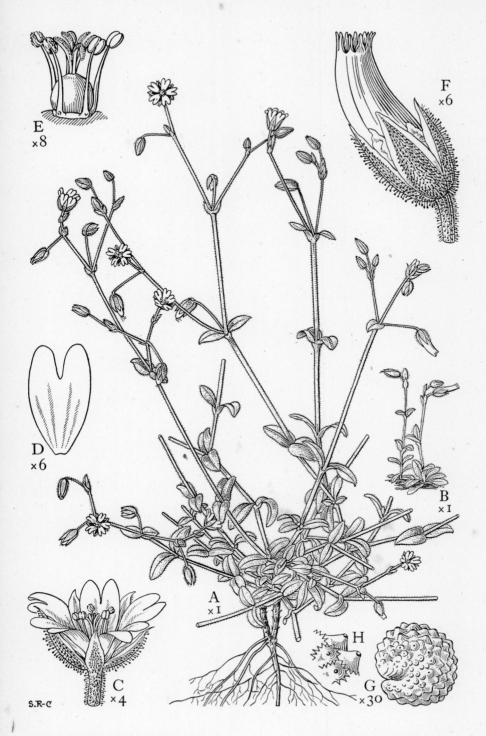

Cerastium pumilum Curtis   Mouse-ear Chickweed

A, a large plant with many of the stems cut off near the base; B, a very small plant; C, flower; D, petal; E, androecium and gynoecium; F, dehiscing capsule and persistent calyx and petals; G, seed; H, part of surface of seed much enlarged. Petals white.

v plate 22

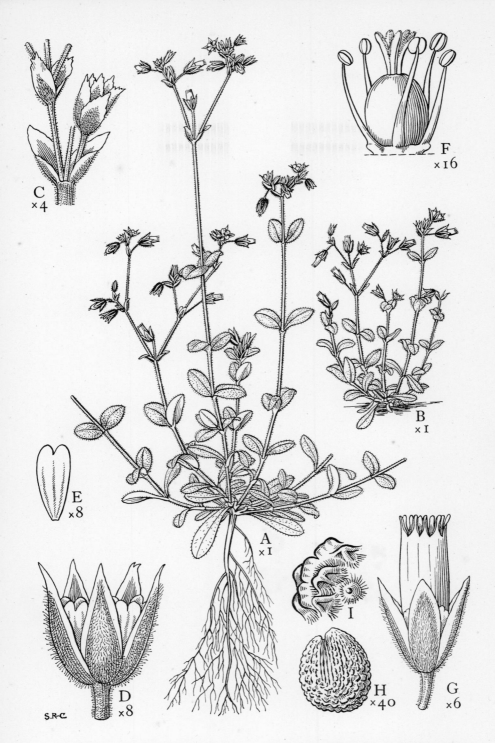

Cerastium semidecandrum L.   Small Mouse-ear Chickweed

A, one of the larger plants, some stems cut off; B, one of the smaller plants; C, part of a flowering stem showing the bracts, which are scarious at margin and apex; D, flower; E, petal; F, androecium and gynoecium; G, dehiscing capsule and persistent calyx and petals; H, seed; I, part of surface of seed much enlarged.
Petals white.

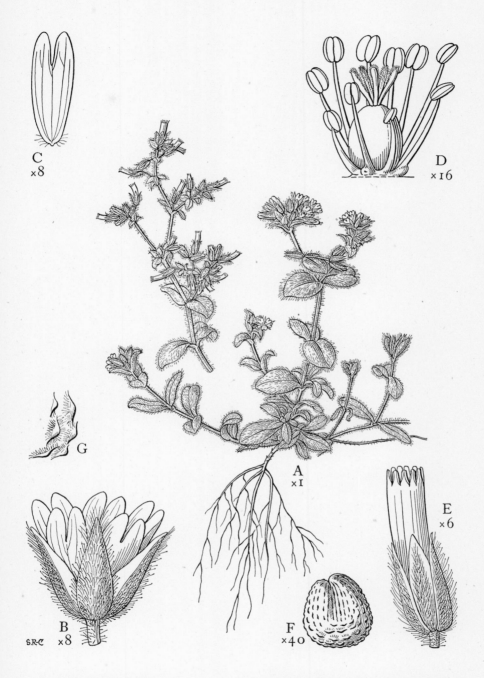

C
×8

D
×16

G

A
×1

B
×8

S.R.C

F
×40

E
×6

Cerastium viscosum L.   Broad-leaved Mouse-ear Chickweed
(syn. *C. glomeratum* Thuill.)

A, flowering plant and upper part of a fruiting stem; B, flower; C, petal; D, androe-cium and gynoecium; E, dehiscing capsule and persistent calyx; F, seed; G, part of surface of seed much enlarged.
Petals white.

v   plate 24

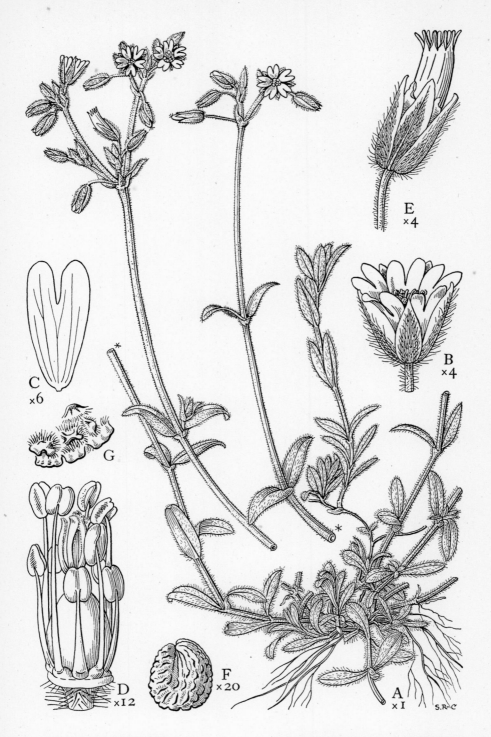

Cerastium vulgatum L.   Common Mouse-ear Chickweed
(syn. *C. triviale* Link; *C. holosteoides* [Fr.] Hyl.)

A, basal part of flowering plant and upper part of two stems; B, flower; C, petal;
D, androecium and gynoecium; E, dehiscing capsule and persistent calyx and petals;
F, seed; G, part of surface of seed much enlarged.
Petals white.

B
×3

C
×4

A
×I

F

E
×20

S.R-C

D
×4

Cerastium alpinum L.   Alpine Chickweed

A, flowering and fruiting plants; B, petal; C, androecium and gynoecium; D, dehiscing capsule and persistent calyx and petals; E, seed; F, part of surface of seed much enlarged.
Petals white.

v   plate 26

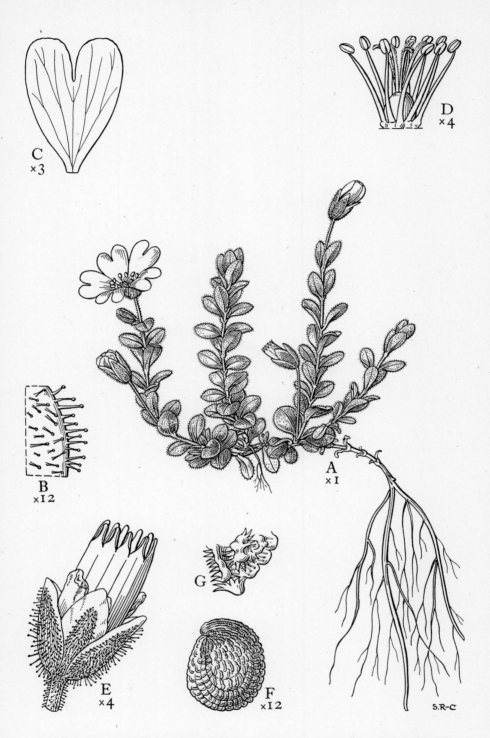

Cerastium nigrescens Edmondst. ex Wats.   Shetland Chickweed

A, plant in flower and fruit; B, part of margin and lower surface of leaf (upper surface more sparsely glandular); C, petal; D, androecium and gynoecium; E, dehiscing capsule and persistent calyx and petals; F, seed; G, part of surface of seed much enlarged.
Petals white.

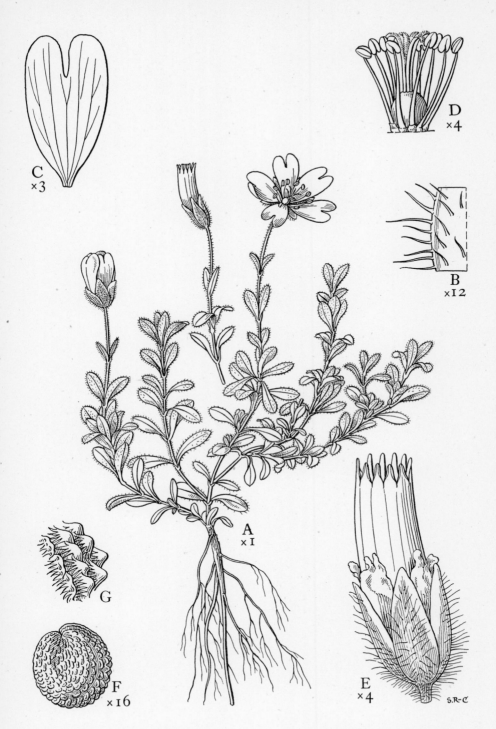

Cerastium arcticum Lange   Highland Chickweed

A, flowering plant and upper part of a fruiting stem; B, part of margin and lower surface of leaf (hairs very sparse or none on upper surface of lower leaves); C, petal; D, androecium and gynoecium; E, dehiscing capsule and persistent calyx and petals; F, seed; G, part of surface of seed much enlarged.
Petals white.

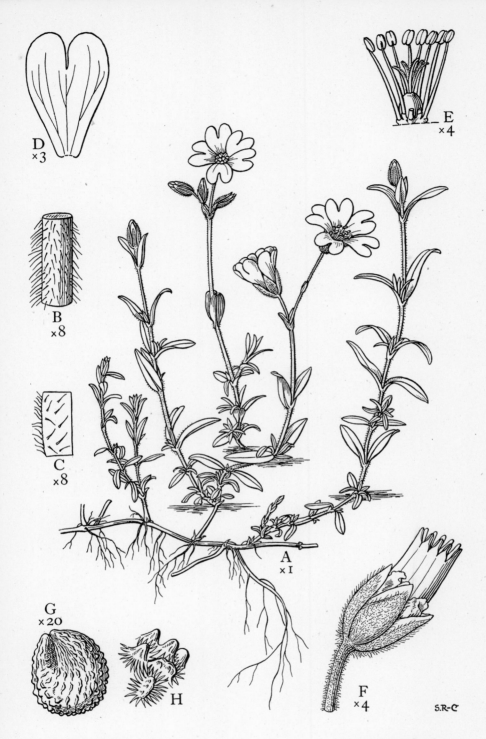

Cerastium arvense L.   Field Chickweed

A, flowering plant; B, part of stem; C, part of margin and upper surface of leaf (lower surface glabrous except the midrib); D, petal; E, androecium, two stamens cut off near the base, and gynoecium; F, dehiscing capsule and persistent calyx and petals; G, seed; H, part of surface of seed much enlarged.
Petals white.

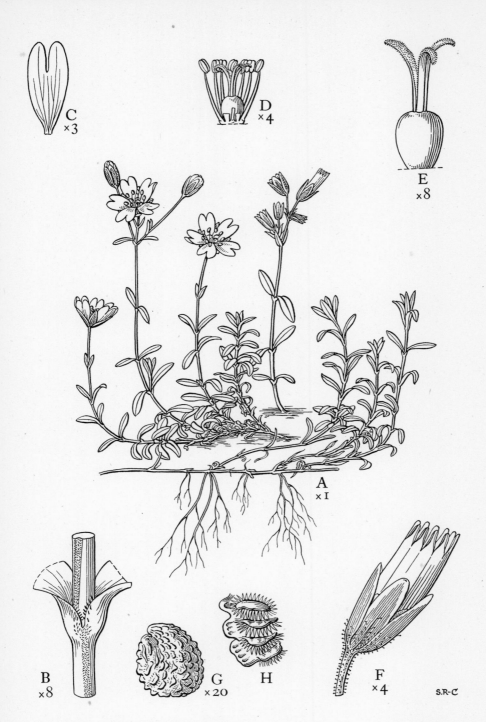

Cerastium cerastoides (L.) Britton   Chickweed
(syn. *C. trigynum* Vill.)

A, plants in flower and fruit, and part of a sterile plant; B, part of stem with bases of
a pair of leaves; C, petal; D, androecium and gynoecium, three stamens and two
petals cut off near the base; E, gynoecium; F, dehiscing capsule and persistent calyx
and petals; G, seed; H, part of surface of seed much enlarged.
Petals white. Styles three or four.

Moenchia erecta (L.) Gaertn. Mey. & Scherb.
(syn. *Cerastium quaternellum* Fenzl)

A, plants in flower and fruit; B, part of flowering stem; C, flower; D, petal; E, androecium, base of two petals, and gynoecium; F, dehiscing capsule and persistent calyx and petal; G, seed; H, part of surface of seed much enlarged.
Petals white.

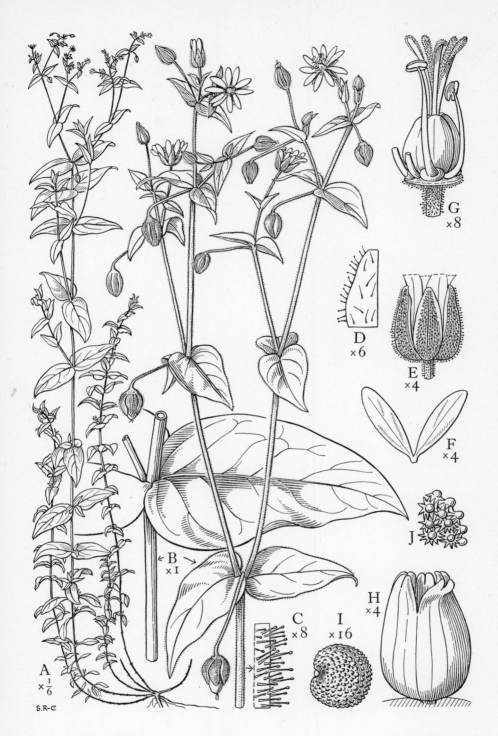

Myosoton aquaticum (L.) Moench   Water Stitchwort

(syn. *Stellaria aquatica* [L.] Scop.; *Malachium aquaticum* [L.] Fr.)

A, plant; B, upper part of a branch and a pair of leaves from lower part of stem;
C, part of a stem; D, part of margin and upper surface of leaf from flowering branch
(both surfaces are alike); E, calyx and base of petals; F, petal; G, part of androecium
and the gynoecium; H, dehiscing capsule; I, seed; J, part of surface of seed much
enlarged.
Petals white, anthers pale blue.

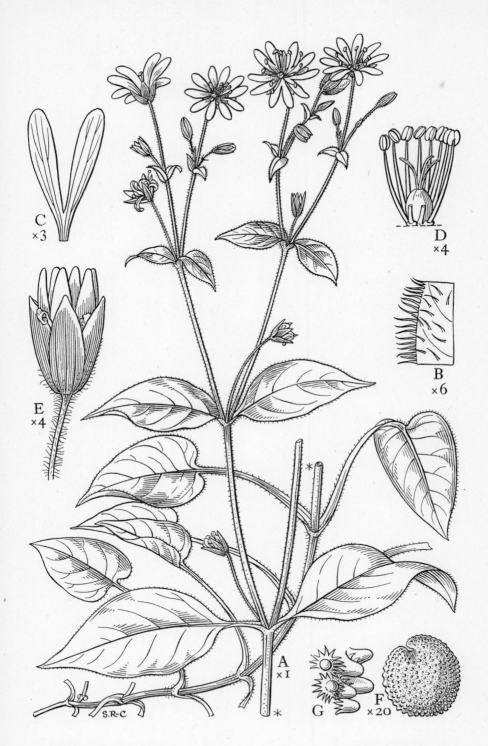

Stellaria nemorum L. Wood Stitchwort

A, flowering plant; B, part of margin and upper surface of leaf; C, petal; D, androecium, two stamens cut off near the base, and gynoecium; E, dehiscing capsule and persistent calyx and petals; F, seed; G, part of surface of seed much enlarged.
Petals white. Leaves pubescent to sparsely pubescent, often glabrescent.

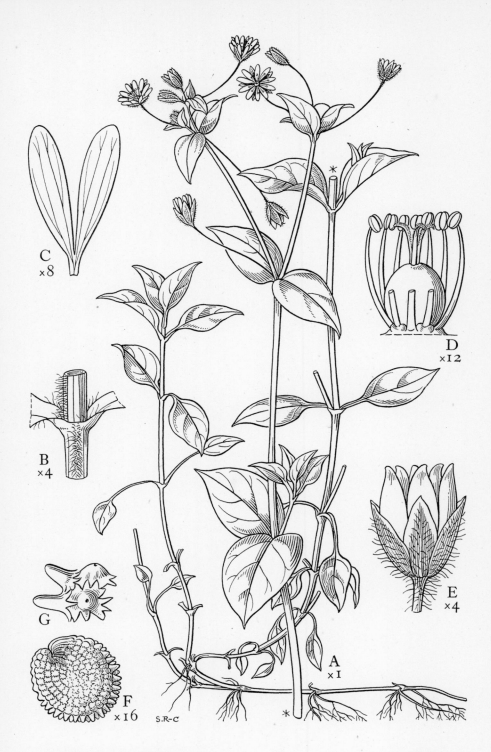

C ×8

D ×12

B ×4

E ×4

G

F ×16

A ×1

S.R-C

Stellaria neglecta Weihe   Stitchwort

A, plant in flower and fruit; B, part of stem with bases of a pair of leaves; C, petal;
D, androecium, three stamens cut off near the base, and gynoecium; E, dehiscing
capsule and persistent calyx; F, seed; G, part of surface of seed much enlarged.
Petals white.

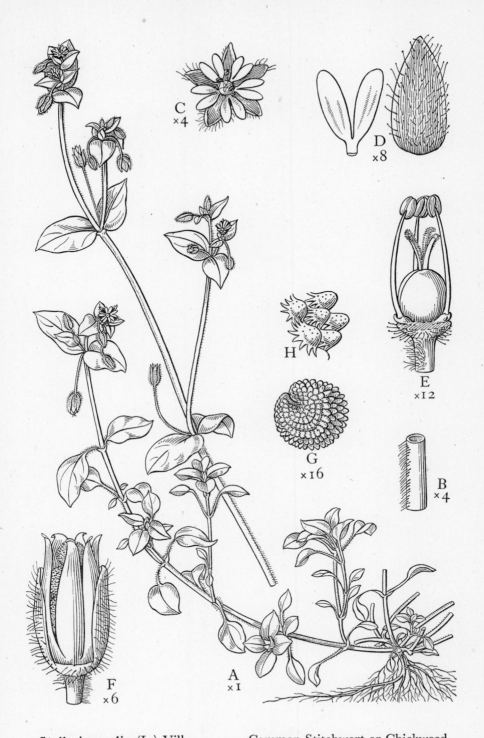

Stellaria media (L.) Vill. Common Stitchwort or Chickweed

A, basal part of plant and upper part of a shoot in flower and fruit; B, part of stem; C, flower; D, sepal, outer surface, and petal; E, androecium and gynoecium; F, dehiscing capsule and persistent calyx, two sepals removed; G, seed; H, part of surface of seed much enlarged.

Petals white, anthers blue-black.

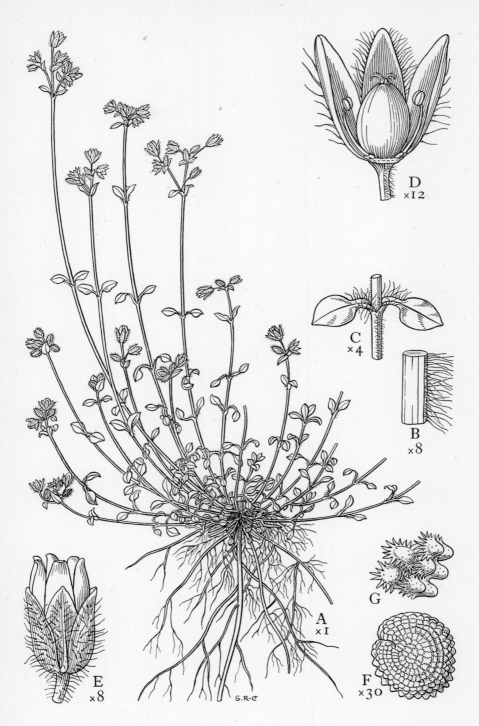

D
×12

C
×4

B
×8

A
×1

E
×8

S·R·C

G

F
×30

Stellaria apetala Ucria   Apetalous Stitchwort
(syn. *S. boraeana* Jord.)

A, plant; B, part of stem; C, part of stem and pair of leaves; D, flower, two sepals
removed; E, dehiscing capsule and persistent calyx; F, seed; G, part of surface of
seed much enlarged.
The species is said to have three stamens, but all flowers dissected had two stamens.

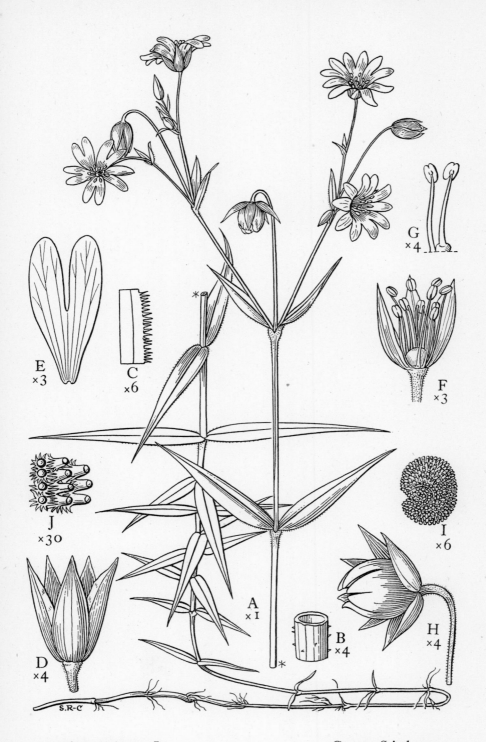

Stellaria holostea L.   Greater Stitchwort

A, plant; B, section of stem; C, part of margin of leaf; D, calyx; E, petal; F, flower, two sepals and all the petals removed; G, stamens; H, dehiscing capsule and persistent calyx; I, seed; J, part of surface of seed.
Petals white.

v   plate 37

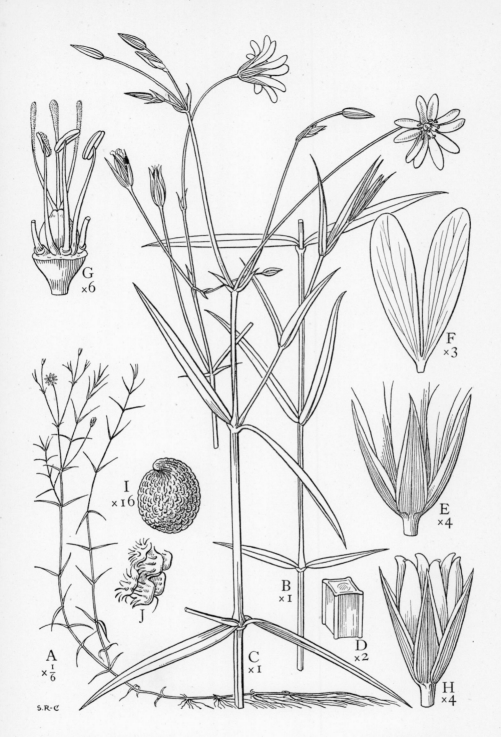

Stellaria palustris Retz.   Marsh Stitchwort
(syn. *S. glauca* With.; *S. dilleniana* Moench)

A, plant; B, lowest third of flowering stem; C, upper part of flowering stems; D, section from middle part of stem; E, calyx and base of petals; F, petal; G, part of androecium and the gynoecium; H, dehiscing capsule and persistent calyx; I, seed; J, part of surface of seed much enlarged.
Petals white.

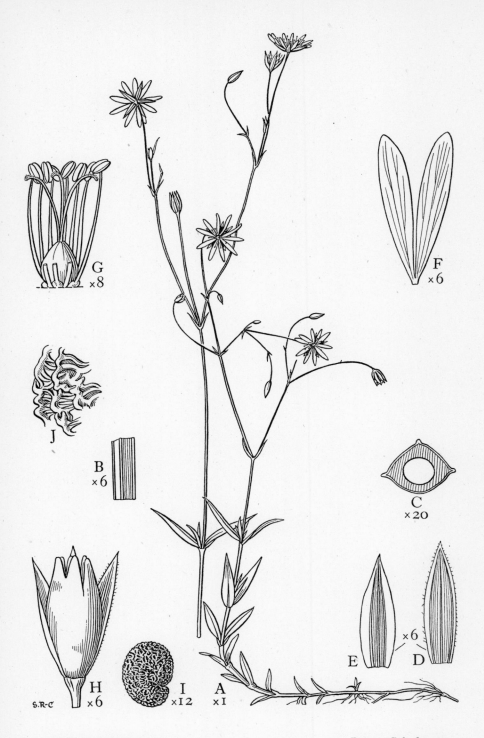

Stellaria graminea L. Lesser Stitchwort

A, a plant and upper part of a flowering stem; B, part of stem; C, transverse section of stem; D and E, outer and inner sepals, inner surface; F, petal; G, androecium, three stamens cut off near the base, and gynoecium; H, dehiscing capsule and persistent calyx, two sepals removed; I, seed; J, part of surface of seed much enlarged. Petals white.

v plate 39

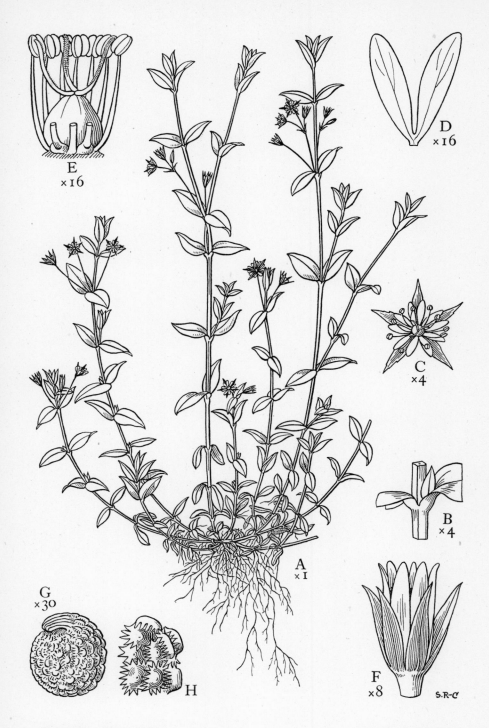

Stellaria alsine Grimm.
(syn. *S. uliginosa* Murr.)

Bog Stitchwort

A, plant; B, part of stem with bases of a pair of leaves; C, flower; D, petal; E, androecium, three stamens cut off above the base, and gynoecium; F, dehiscing capsule
and persistent calyx; G, seed; H, part of surface of seed much enlarged.
Petals white.

v   plate 40

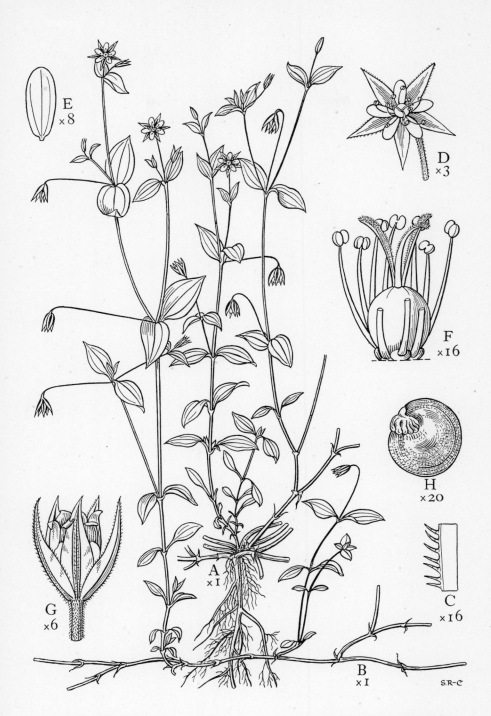

Arenaria trinervia L.   Three-nerved Sandwort

A, part of a plant in flower and fruit; B, one of the trailing prostrate stems, and ascending flowering stems; C, part of margin of leaf; D, flower; E, petal; F, androecium, upper part of three stamens cut off, and gynoecium; G, dehiscing capsule and persistent calyx and petals; H, seed.
Petals white.   Stems finely puberulous.

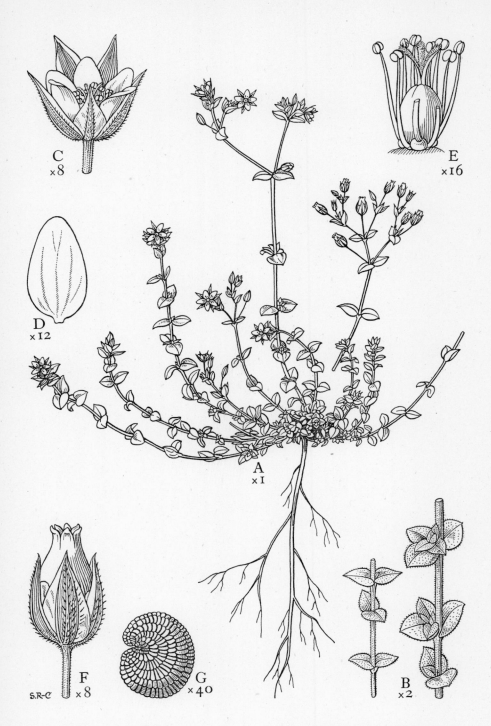

Arenaria serpyllifolia L.   Thyme-leaved Sandwort

A, flowering plant, and upper part of a fruiting stem; B, part of a robust and a weaker leafy stem; C, flower; D, petal; E, androecium, the upper part of two stamens cut off, and gynoecium; F, dehiscing capsule and persistent calyx and petals—the capsule may be less flask-shaped; G, seed.
Petals white.

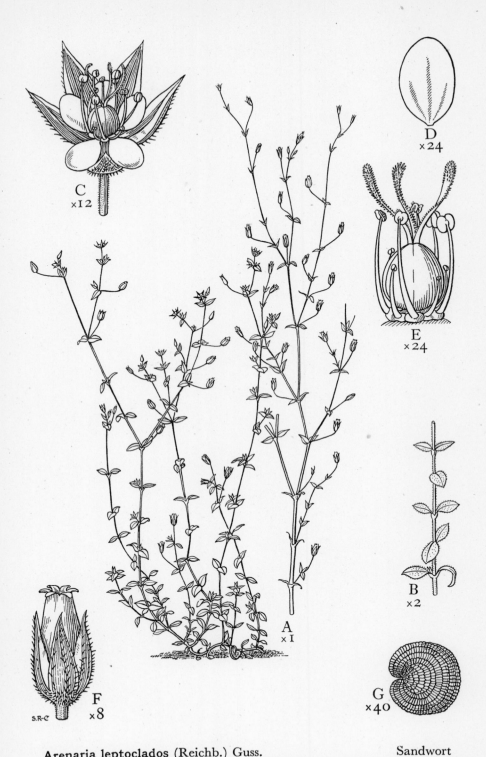

Arenaria leptoclados (Reichb.) Guss.   Sandwort

A, a plant, and a fruiting stem from a taller plant; B, lower part of a stem; C, flower;
D, petal; E, androecium and gynoecium; F, dehiscing capsule and persistent calyx;
G, seed.
Petals white, anthers turning pink at dehiscence.

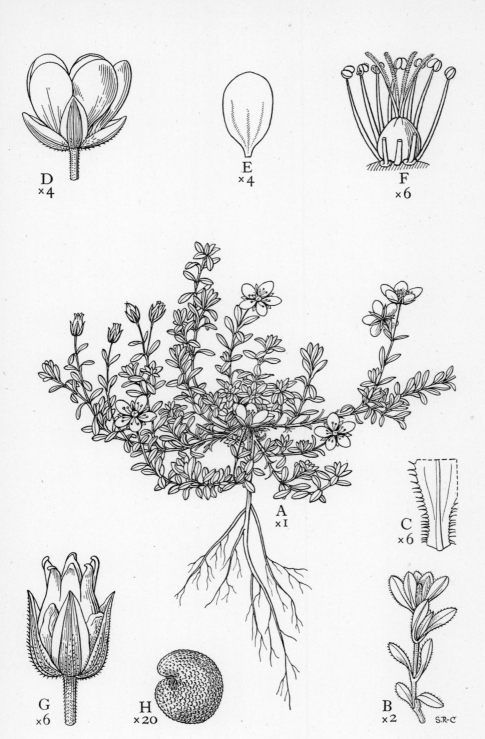

Arenaria ciliata L.   Fringed Sandwort

A, plant; B, part of a leafy stem; C, lower part of a leaf; D, flower; E, petal; F, androecium, three stamens cut off, and gynoecium; G, dehiscing capsule and persistent calyx and petals; H, seed.
Petals white.

v   plate 44

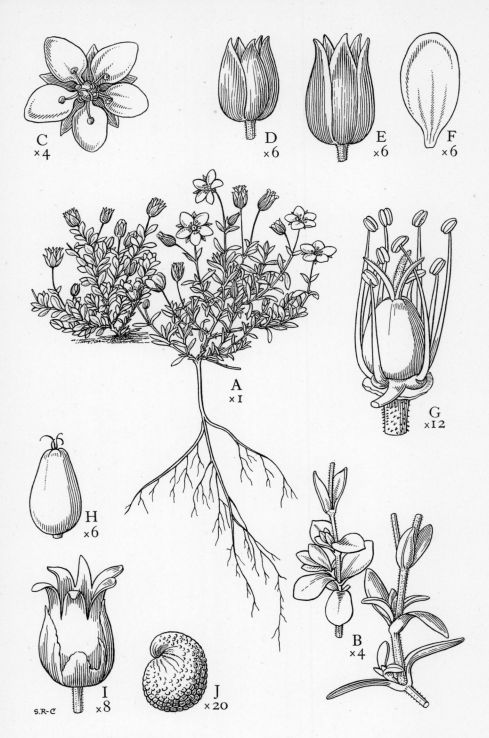

C
×4

D
×6

E
×6

F
×6

A
×1

G
×12

H
×6

I
×8

J
×20

B
×4

S.R-C

Arenaria norvegica Gunn.   Sandwort
(syn. *A. gothica* Fries)

A, two plants to show variation in the species; B, leafy stems from the plants in fig.
A; C, flower; D, calyx from broad-leaved plant; E, calyx from narrow-leaved plant;
F, petal; G, androecium, one stamen cut off, and gynoecium; H, immature capsule;
I, dehiscing capsule and remains of calyx; J, seed.
Petals white. *A. gothica* seems to be no more than a variant of a variable species for
which the oldest name is *A. norvegica*.

v   plate 45

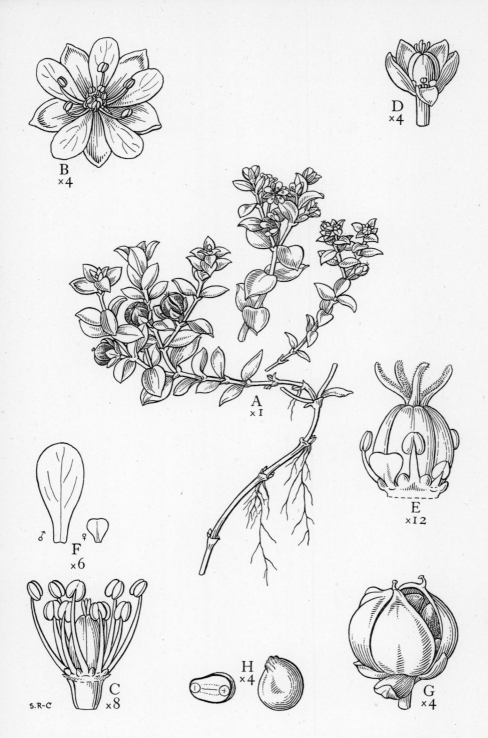

Arenaria peploides L.   Sea Purslane

(syn. *Honkenya peploides* [L.] Ehrh.)

A, fruiting plant and flowering stems from other plants; B, male flower; C, androecium and gynoecium from male flower; D, female flower; E, one petal, androecium, and gynoecium from female flower; F, petals; G, calyx and dehiscing capsule; H, seed, and transverse section of same.

Petals greenish-white.

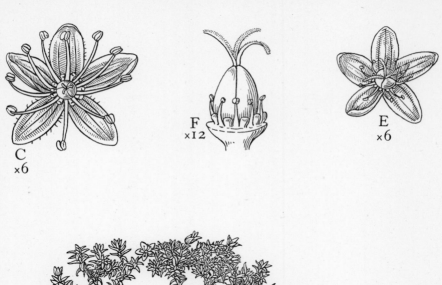

S.R-C

Arenaria sedoides (L.) F. J. Hanb.   Mossy Cyphel
(syn. *Cherleria sedoides* L.; *Alsine cherleria* Fenzl)

A, plants; B, a leafy stem; C, male flower; D, androecium (upper part of four stamens cut off) and gynoecium from male flower; E, female flower; F, androecium and gynoecium from female flower; G, upper part of fruiting stem; H, seed.
Petals absent, or present in male flowers and very reduced, white.

v plate 47

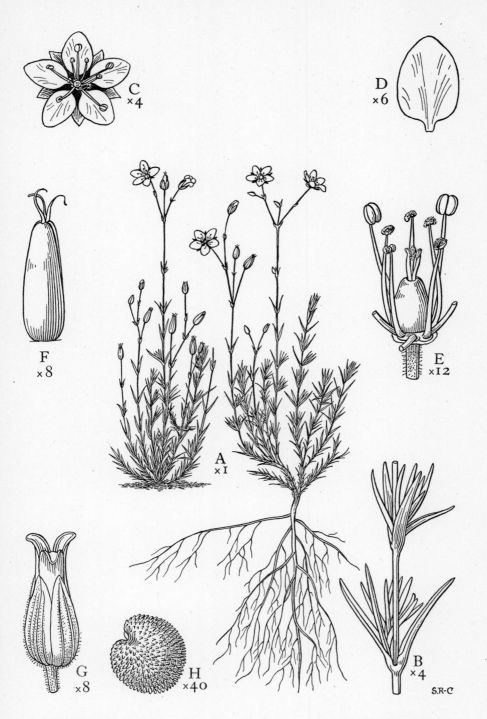

Arenaria verna L.   Spring Sandwort

A, plants in flower and fruit; B, part of a leafy stem; C, flower; D, petal; E, androecium, three stamens cut off near the base, and gynoecium; F, capsule before
dehiscence; G, dehiscing capsule and persistent calyx; H, seed.
Petals white, anthers pink. Stems minutely puberulous. Styles and capsule-valves
said to be three, four, or five but three in all material examined.

v   plate 48

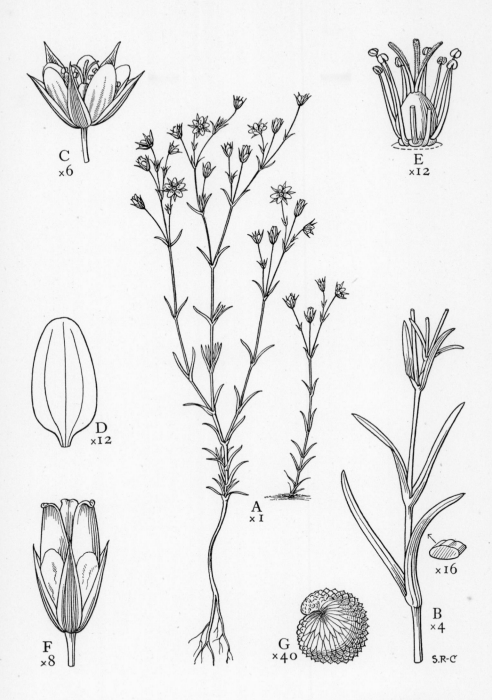

Arenaria tenuifolia L.   Fine-leaved Sandwort

A, two plants; B, part of a leafy stem, and section of a leaf; C, flower; D, petal; E, androecium, upper part of two stamens cut off, and gynoecium; F, dehiscing capsule with persistent calyx and petals; G, seed.
Petals white.

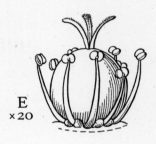

C
×8

E
×20

D
×12

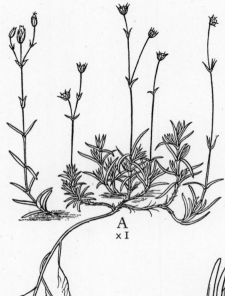

A
×1

F
×8

S.R.C

G
×40

×12

B
×4

Arenaria uliginosa Schlecht.   Bog Sandwort

(syn. *Minuartia stricta* [Sw.] Hiern)

A, plants in flower and fruit; B, part of a leafy stem, and transverse section of a leaf;
C, flower; D, petal; E, androecium and gynoecium; F, dehiscing capsule and persistent
calyx and petals; G, seed.
Petals white.

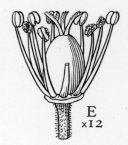

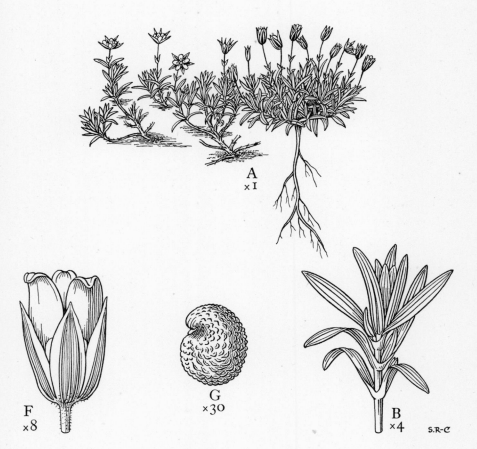

Arenaria rubella (Wahlenb.) Sm.   Mountain Sandwort
(syn. *Alsine rubella* Wahlenb.)

A, plants in flower and fruit; B, leafy stem; C, flower; D, petal; E, androecium, upper part of one stamen cut off, and gynoecium; F, dehiscing capsule and persistent calyx and petals; G, seed.

Calyx tinged with red, petals white, anthers pink. Styles and capsule-valves three or four.

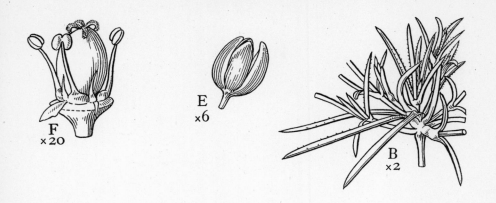
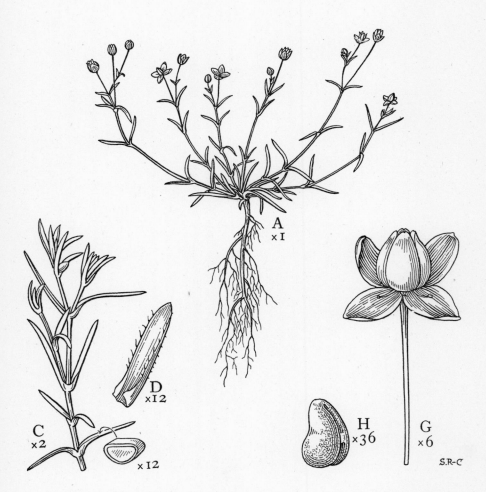

Sagina maritima Sm.   Sea Pearlwort

A, plant; B, part of a rosette; C, a young stem, and section of a leaf; D, one of the uppermost leaves; E, a bud; F, flower with calyx removed, two rudimentary petals are visible; G, calyx and capsule; H, seed.

Petals usually absent, when present very small and white.

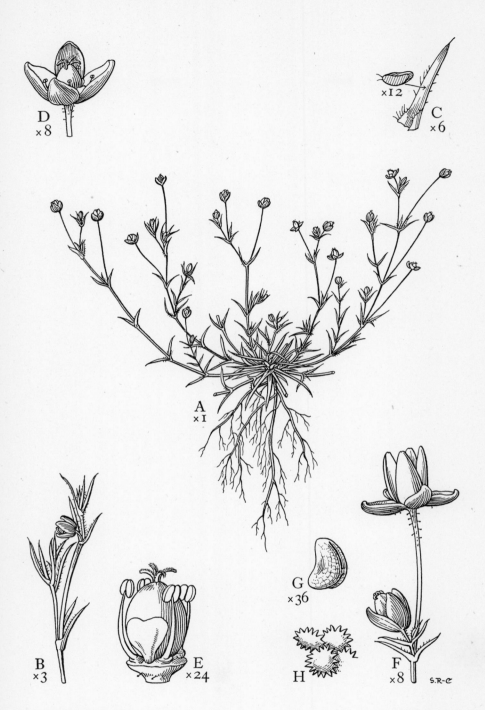

Sagina apetala Ard.   Pearlwort

A, plant; B, upper part of a flowering stem; C, leaf and transverse section of same;
D, flower; E, flower, calyx and three petals removed; F, upper part of fruiting stem;
G, seed; H, part of surface of seed, much enlarged.
Petals white, often absent.

v   plate 53

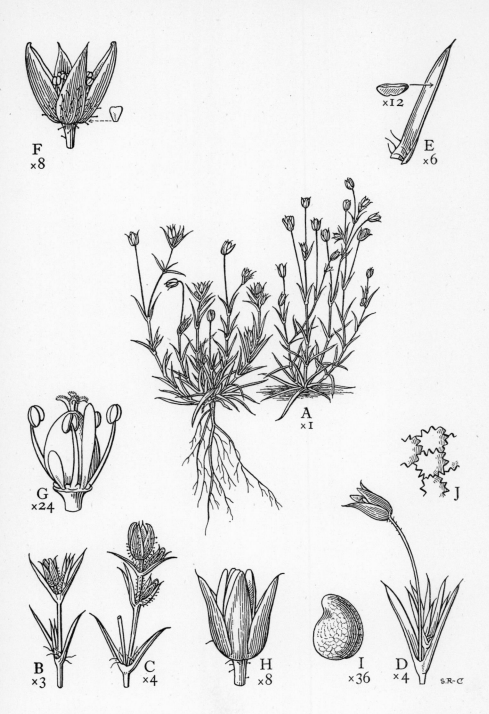

Sagina ciliata Fr.   Pearlwort

A, plants; B and C, upper part of flowering stems; D, immature fruit and upper part
of stem; E, leaf, and transverse section of same; F, flower, and a petal; G, flower, the
calyx and two petals removed; H, calyx and capsule; I, seed; J, part of surface of seed,
much enlarged.
Petals white, very small and variable in shape, or absent. Plants are not uncommonly
glabrescent, and may be almost or quite glabrous from the beginning.

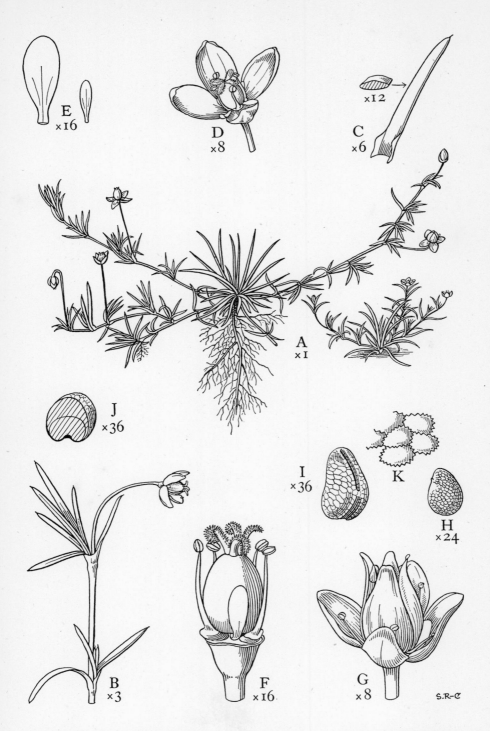

Sagina procumbens L.　　　　　　　　　Common Pearlwort

A, plants; B, part of a flowering stem; C, rosette leaf and transverse section of same;
D, flower; E, petals from different flowers; F, androecium and gynoecium with one
petal; G, dehiscing capsule and persistent calyx, petals, and stamens; H, seed; I,
seed in three-quarter back view; J, transverse section of lower part of seed; K, part of
surface of seed much enlarged.
Petals white. The petals are sometimes absent.

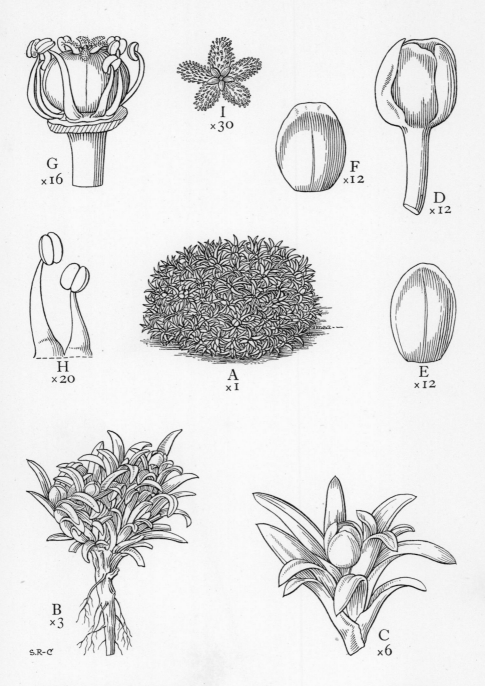

G ×16

I ×30

F ×12

D ×12

H ×20

A ×1

E ×12

B ×3

S·R·C

C ×6

Sagina boydii F. B. White   Pearlwort

A, a number of plants forming a cushion; B, a plant; C, upper part of a flowering stem;
D, flower with 4-lobed calyx; E and F, sepals, outer surface; G, androecium and
gynoecium, the stamens are apparently sterile and may be 8 or 10 in number; H,
stamens; I, stigmas and brown glandular processes.
Petals wanting; calyx may be 5-lobed; fruit and seed not seen.

C
×6

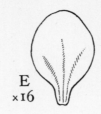

E
×16

D
×8

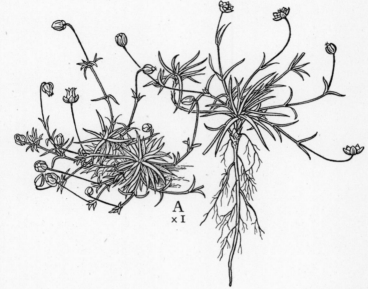

A
×1

B
×4

G
×36

F
×8

S.R-C

Sagina saginoides (L.) Karst.　　　　　　　　Alpine Pearlwort
(syn. *S. linnaei* C. Presl; *S. saxatilis* Wimm.)

A, plants; B, upper part of a flowering stem; C, flower; D, flower, four sepals and
four petals removed; E, petal; F, calyx and dehiscing capsule; G, seed.
Petals white.

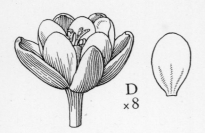

D ×8

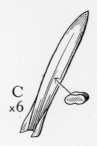

C ×6

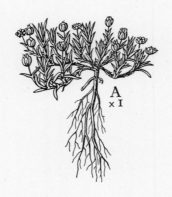

A ×1

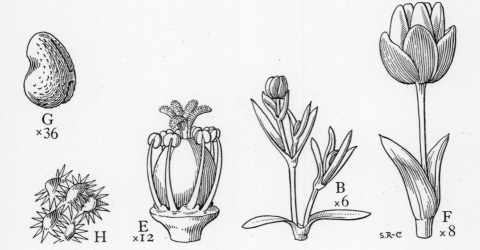

G ×36

H

E ×12

B ×6

S.R-C

F ×8

Sagina intermedia Fenzl   Alpine Pearlwort
(syn. *S. caespitosa* Auct. Angl.; *S. nivalis* Fr.)

A, plant; B, upper part of flowering stem; C, leaf, and transverse section of same; D, flower and petal; E, flower, calyx and petals removed; F, upper part of fruiting stem; G, seed; H, part of surface of seed, much enlarged.
Petals white; stamens variable in number, 7, 8, and 10 in flowers examined.

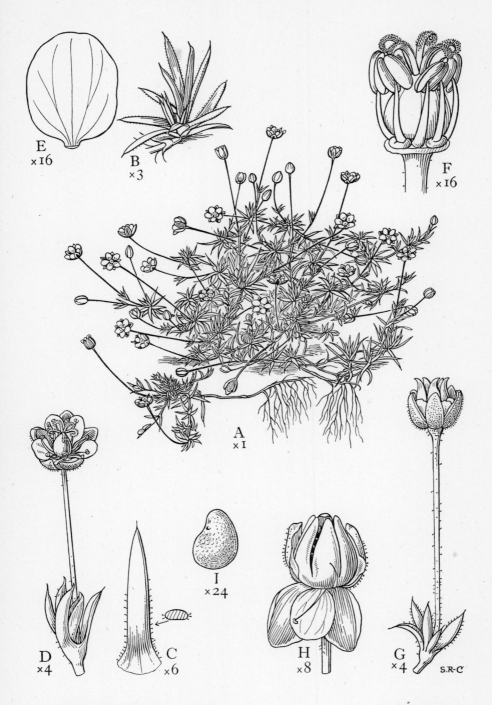

E ×16

B ×3

F ×16

A ×1

D ×4

C ×6

I ×24

H ×8

G ×4

S·R·C

Sagina subulata (Sw.) Presl   Pearlwort

A, flowering plants; B, rosette and base of shoot; C, rosette-leaf, and transverse section of same; D, upper leaves and flower; E, petal; F, androecium and gynoecium; G, upper leaves and fruit; H, capsule and persistent calyx, petals and stamens; I, seed.
Petals white.

Sagina nodosa (L.) Fenzl   Knotted Pearlwort

A, plant, and a fruiting stem; B, leaves on lower part of stem, and transverse section of leaf; C, upper part of stem; D, flower, calyx and petals removed; E, petal; F, calyx and dehiscing capsule; G, seed; H, part of surface of seed, much enlarged. Petals white.

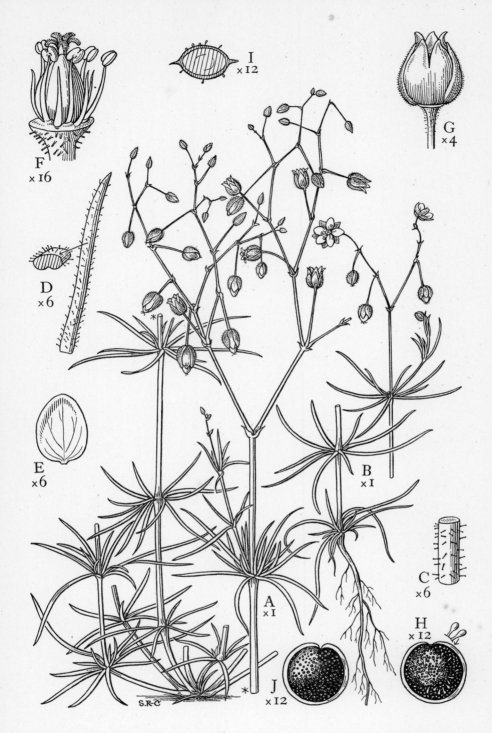

Spergula arvensis L.   Corn Spurrey
(syn. *S. vulgaris* Boenn.; *S. sativa* Boenn.)

A, a fruiting plant; B, lower and upper parts of a small flowering plant; C, part of stem;
D, leaf from upper part of stem, and transverse section of same; E, petal; F, flower,
calyx and petals removed; G, capsule and part of calyx; H, seed, and two of the
papillae enlarged; I, transverse section of seed; J, epapillose seed (*S. sativa* Boenn.).
Petals white; plant finely puberulous, or more or less glabrous in the lower part.

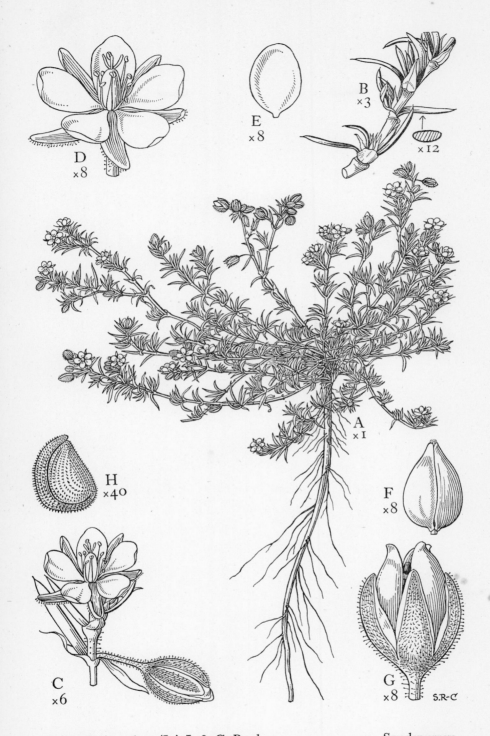

Spergularia rubra (L.) J. & C. Presl   Sandspurrey

A, plant; B, part of leafy stem, and section of leaf; C, apex of a flowering stem; D, flower; E, petal; F, immature capsule; G, calyx and dehiscing capsule; H, seed. Petals cobalt-violet or pinkish-violet, gynoecium yellow.

v   plate 62

Spergularia bocconi (Scheele) Merino   Sandspurrey
(syn. *S. atheniensis* Aschers.; *S. campestris* [Kindb.] Willk. & Lge.)

A, plant, many of the stems cut off; B, part of a leafy stem, and transverse section of a leaf; C, flower; D, petal; E, part of a fruiting stem; F, calyx, petals, and dehiscing capsule; G, seed.

Petals rose, white at the base.

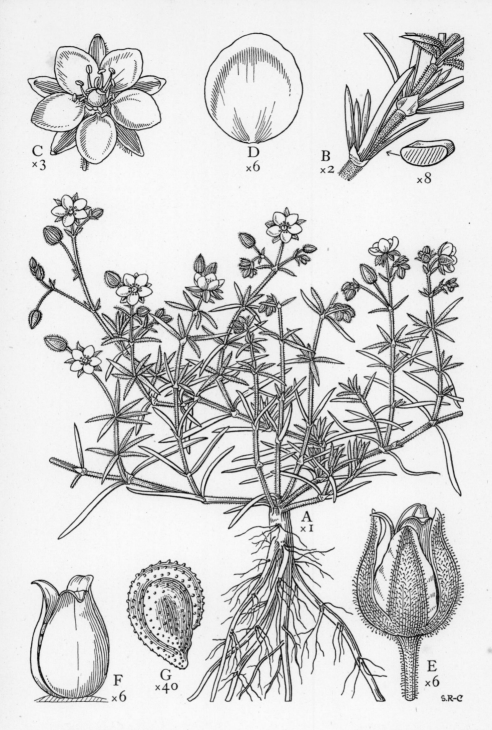

C ×3   D ×6   B ×2   ×8

A ×I

F ×6   G ×40   E ×6

S.R-C

Spergularia rupicola Lebel   Sea Sandspurrey
(syn. *S. rupestris* Lebel non Cambess.)

A, plant; B, part of leafy stem, and section of leaf; C, flower; D, petal; E, upper part of
pedicel, calyx, and dehiscing capsule; F, capsule; G, seed.
Petals cobalt-violet.

v   plate 64

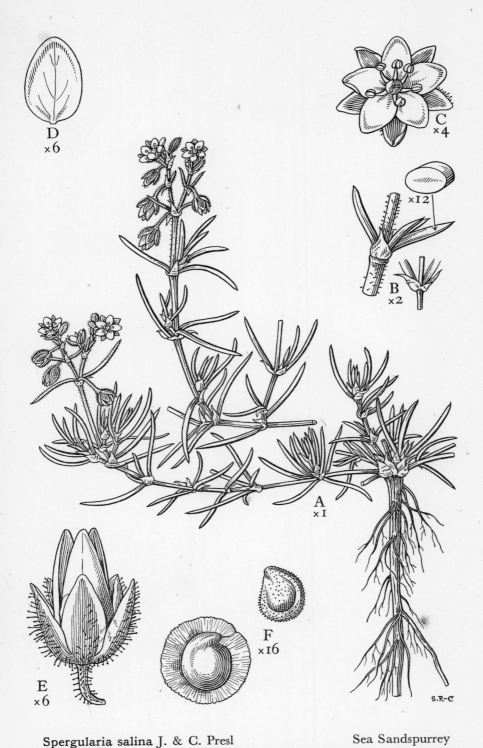

Spergularia salina J. & C. Presl   Sea Sandspurrey

A, part of a plant, one of the flowering and fruiting branches detached and several
stems cut off near the base; B, parts of leafy branches, and transverse section of a leaf;
C, flower; D, petal; E, calyx and dehiscing capsule; F, winged and unwinged seeds.
Petals purplish-rose, white at base.

C ×4   D ×6   B ×2   ×12   A ×1   E ×6   F ×16

S.R.C

Spergularia marginata (DC.) Kittel   Sea Sandspurrey
(syn. *S. media* auct.)

A, flowering plant (plants may be more elongated and straggly and pedicels may be longer); B, part of leafy stem, and section of leaf; C, flower; D, petal; E, calyx and capsule; F, seed.
Petals violet-rose or violet-cobalt, whitish towards the centre. Plants may be quite glabrous or more or less glandular (var. *glandulosa* Druce).

v plate 66

INDEX